WICKED JOKES

Spooky Jokes

Created by Magpie Books,
an imprint of Constable & Robinson Ltd

Cover design and inside illustrations
courtesy of Mike Phillips

This is a Parragon Book
This edition published in 2005

Parragon
Queen Street House
4 Queen Street
Bath BA1 1HE,UK

Copyright © Parragon 2002

ISBN 1-40546-129-2
Printed in China

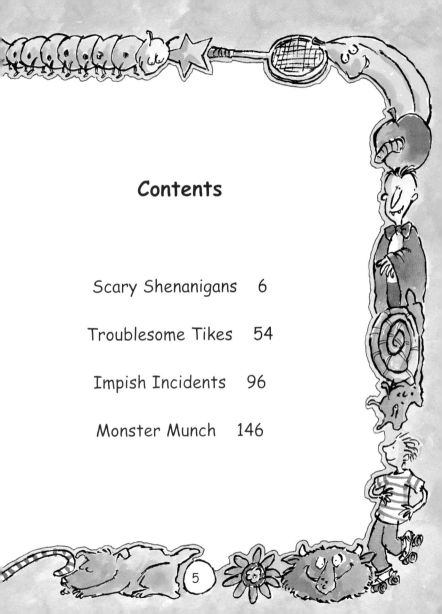

Contents

SCARY SHENANIGANS

6

When does a ghost have breakfast?
In the moaning.

Why couldn't the ghost go on the bus?
He didn't have the correct chains.

Why do ghosts shiver and moan?
You'd do the same if you had to walk around under a sheet all day.

Where do spirits go for a suntan?
The Ghosta Brava.

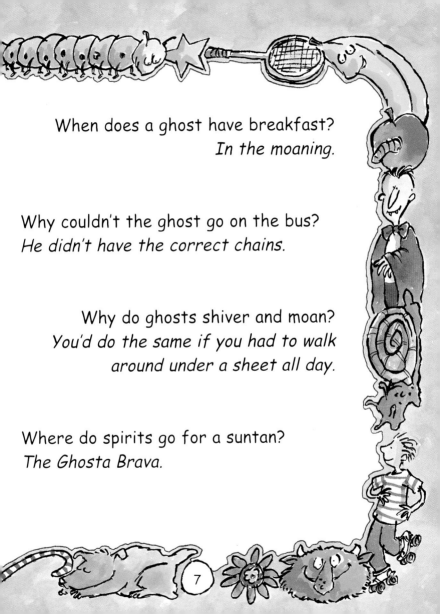

How do you make a milkshake?
Sneak up behind a glass of milk and yell, "Boo!"

What goes, "Cackle, cackle, splat!"?
A witch flying into a lamppost.

What is a ghost's favourite bird?
A scare crow.

What does a ghost have with fish
and chips?
R. I. Peas.

What's creamy and chocolaty and can
read the future?
Éclair-voyant.

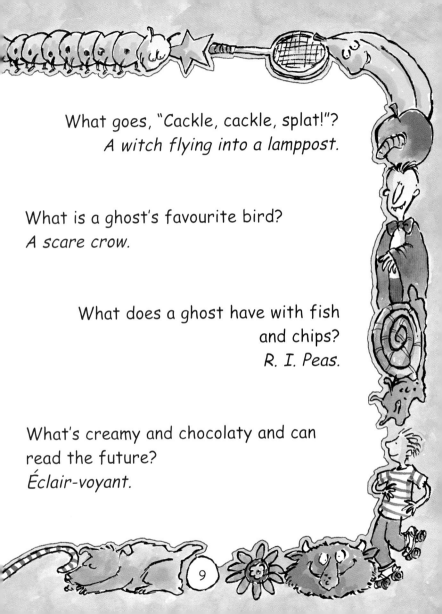

What does a witch's cat say at Halloween?
"Trick or trout?"

Where do baby ghosts go during the day?
Dayscare centres.

What's the most important programme on a witch's computer?
The spell checker.

What do you call an owl with a toupee?
Hedwig.

What do you get when you cross
Bambi with a ghost?
Bamboo.

What trees do witches plant in
their gardens?
Brooms.

What should you say when you meet
a ghost?
"How do you boo, sir, how do you boo?"

What goes, "Cackle, cackle, crackle."?
A witch spontaneously combusting.

Where do witches have their temples?
Either side of their head.

What did the mother ghost say to the baby ghost?
"Put your boos and shocks on."

What story do little ghosts like to hear at bedtime?
Ghouldilocks and the three scares.

Who's in charge of the ghost detectives?
The chief inspectre.

Why couldn't the witch fly for long distances?
She got broomsick.

How do ghosts keep fit?
By regular exorcise.

What do ghosts drink at breakfast?
Coffee with scream and sugar.

What's the difference between a witch and the letters m, a, k, e and s?
One makes spells and the other spells makes.

Why did the wizard get into the fridge?
He was in for a cold spell.

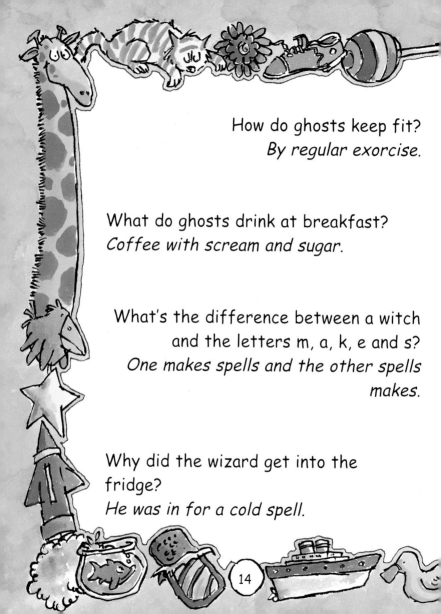

14

Who do witches share flats with?
Their broommates.

What vehicle does a kid ghost like
to ride?
A boocycle.

When do ghosts go to work?
Moandays to Frightdays.

Did you hear about the Daffy Duck
witch?
She kept having Disney spells.

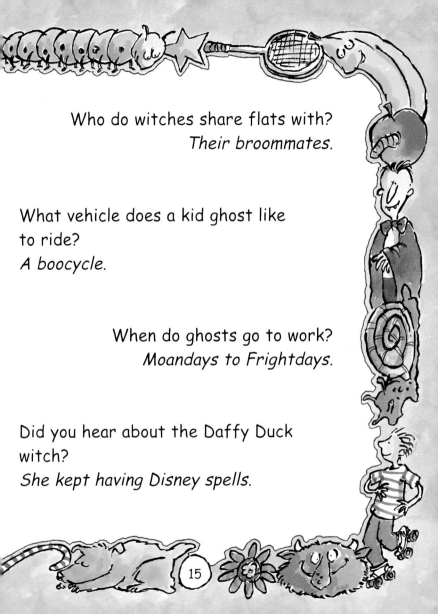

15

What are a ghouls best friend?
Demons.

What do ghosts eat for dinner?
Spook-ghetti.

What's the best way to imagine you're
flying on a broomstick?
Witchful thinking.

Where do phantoms mail their letters?
At the ghost office.

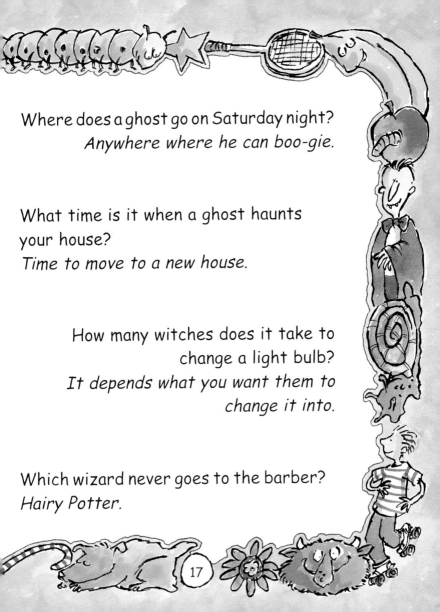

Where does a ghost go on Saturday night?
Anywhere where he can boo-gie.

What time is it when a ghost haunts
your house?
Time to move to a new house.

How many witches does it take to
change a light bulb?
*It depends what you want them to
change it into.*

Which wizard never goes to the barber?
Hairy Potter.

What do you get if you cross a cocker spaniel, a poodle and a ghost?
A cocker-poodle-boo.

Why did the witch take a week to make a spell?
It was a slow-motion-potion.

How do ghosts start their cars?
With spook plugs.

What do you call a wizard with dandruff?
A blizzard.

What happens when a ghost gets lost
in the fog?
He is mist.

What do ghosts use to wash their hair?
Sham-boo.

What do ghosts drink with their meals?
Whine.

Why couldn't the ghost get a whisky in
the pub?
They didn't serve spirits.

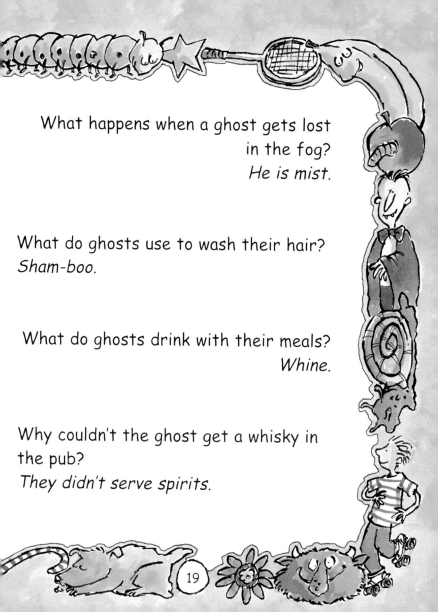

How can you tell when a window is scared?
It gets shudders.

What do phantoms do when they need more coffee on a plane?
Call the air ghostess or the fright attendant.

Why did the wizard wear a pointed hat?
Because he had a pointed head.

What kind of sorceress lives by the sea?
A sandwitch.

What did the witch say to her cat?
"You're familiar."

What happens when ghosts haunt a theatre?
The actors get stage fright.

What is Beethoven doing in his coffin right now?
Decomposing.

What kind of sorceress lives by the sea but is afraid to go swimming?
A chicken sandwitch.

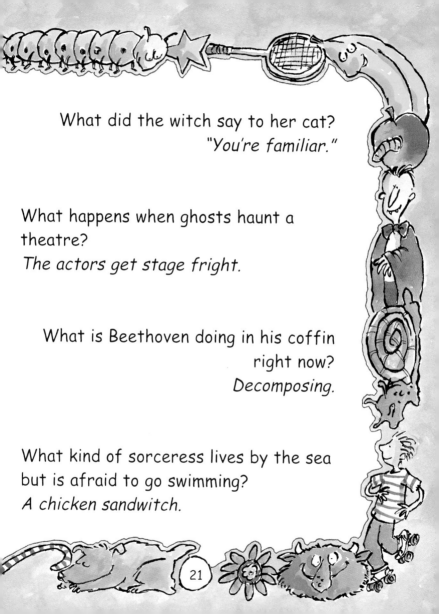

Who is the most famous ghost detective?
Sherlock Moans.

Who is the most famous skeleton detective?
Sherlock Bones.

Who is the most famous wizard detective?
Warlock Holmes.

What do witches take to the beach?
Suntan potion.

Why do ghosts love pubs?
Because of all the boos.

Why was the weather witch so popular?
She was always forecasting sunny spells.

What do you call a haunted chicken?
A poultry-geist.

What do Hawaiian ghosts play?
The spookulele.

Where do ghosts do their homework?
Exorcise books.

How does a wizard's cooking pot
introduce itself?
"Hello, I'm called Ron."

What do you call a spirit novelist?
A ghost writer.

What do you call a spirit playwright?
A crypt writer.

What kind of witch speeds down the
motorway at 100mph?
A road hag.

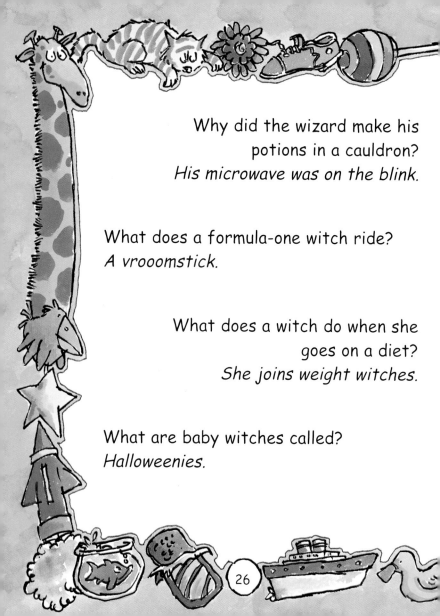

Why did the wizard make his potions in a cauldron?
His microwave was on the blink.

What does a formula-one witch ride?
A vrooomstick.

What does a witch do when she goes on a diet?
She joins weight witches.

What are baby witches called?
Halloweenies.

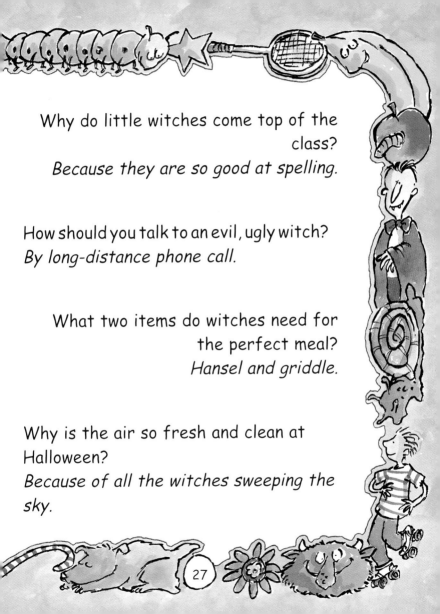

Why do little witches come top of the class?
Because they are so good at spelling.

How should you talk to an evil, ugly witch?
By long-distance phone call.

What two items do witches need for the perfect meal?
Hansel and griddle.

Why is the air so fresh and clean at Halloween?
Because of all the witches sweeping the sky.

What do spooks chant at football matches?
"Here we ghost, here we ghost, here we ghost..."

What's the difference between a deer on the run and a miniature witch?
One's a hunted stag and the other's a stunted hag.

What did the teacher witch do to her terrible pupil?
Ex-spelled her.

Why did the witch poison the boy's cornflakes?
She was a cereal killer.

What do witches sell in art shops?
Witch craft.

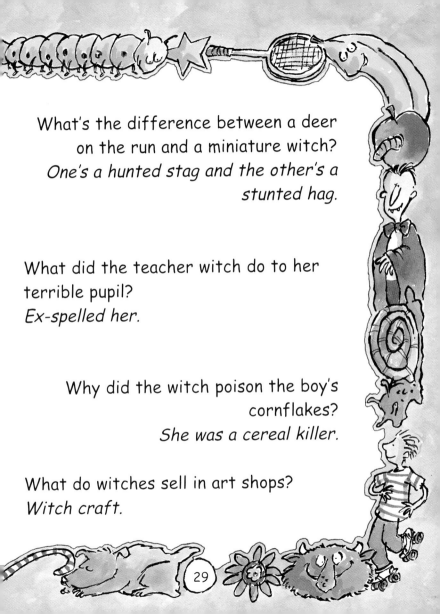

For what crime are ghosts most often sent to prison?
Booglary.

Why did the witch's cat always go to the wizard?
Because sorcerers are often filled with milk.

What kind of make-up do ghosts wear?
Mas-scare-a.

Why don't witches get angry when they're on a broomstick?
They don't want to fly off the handle.

Why did the wizard jump off Nelson's Column?
He wanted to be a big hit in the West End.

What do ghosts play when they're bored?
Moanopoly.

How can you make a tall witch short?
Borrow all her money.

Who protects the shores where spirits live?
The ghostguard.

Why is a witch like a candle?
They are both wicked.

What do baby ghosts wear?
Pillowcases.

Why did the gravedigger steal knickers?
Because he wanted to be an undie-taker.

Why was the woman in love with the ghost?
She was possessed.

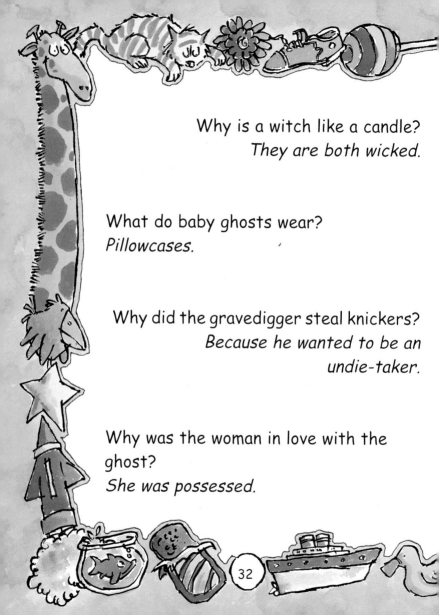

32

What does a ghost have on top of his
apple pie?
Whipped scream.

What kind of music do ghosts like?
Rhythm and boos.

How do you make a witch float?
*Get a couple of scoops of ice cream,
some lemonade and a witch.*

What kind of play do ghosts like to see
at Christmas time?
A phantomime.

How do you get rid of a ghost in your house?
Demand he shares the rent.

Why did the witch give up fortune-telling?
She couldn't see a future in it.

Why do ghosts go to football matches?
They like to boo the referee.

Why was the young ghost so scared?
He heard a human story.

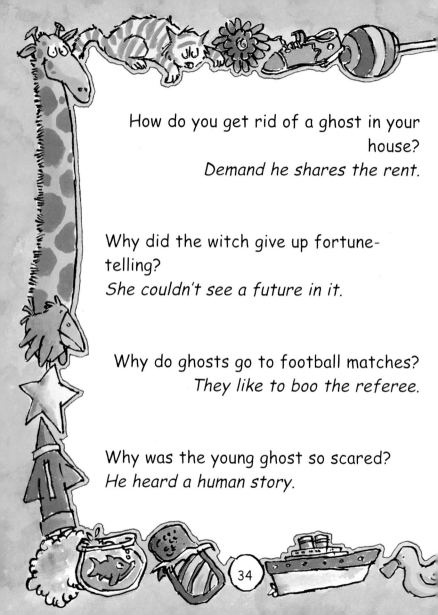

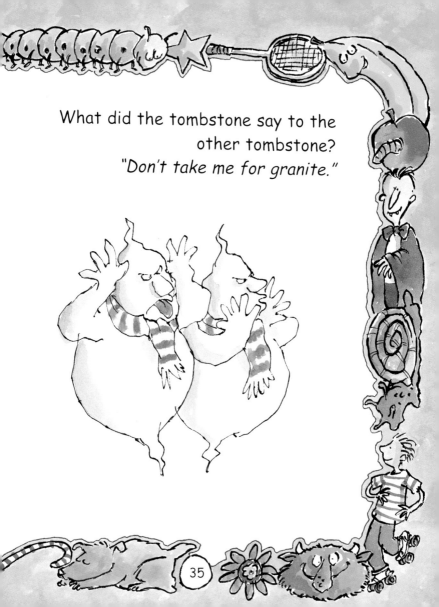

What did the tombstone say to the
other tombstone?
"Don't take me for granite."

What goes, "Oob, oob"?
A ghost reversing.

Why did the witches invite the wizards to their tea party?
Because their cups needed sorcerers.

Why do ghosts only eat the best quality organic food?
Because it's super natural.

What do ghosts do in hospital?
Talk about their apparitions.

How can you make a witch scratch?
Take away the "W".

Who haunts Parliament?
The Spooker of the House.

What did the congregation say when
the witch came down the aisle?
"Here comes the bride and broom!"

Where do ghost trains stop?
At manifestations.

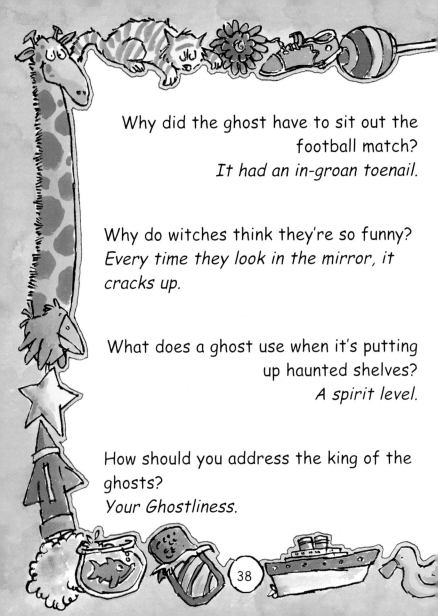

Why did the ghost have to sit out the football match?
It had an in-groan toenail.

Why do witches think they're so funny?
Every time they look in the mirror, it cracks up.

What does a ghost use when it's putting up haunted shelves?
A spirit level.

How should you address the king of the ghosts?
Your Ghostliness.

Why did the ghost listen to the witch's intestines?
It loved the sound of hag pipes.

Which game do ghosts play at parties?
Haunt the thimble.

What has a black hat, flies on a broomstick and can't see?
A witch with her eyes closed.

Where do ghosts like to stay when they go on holiday?
Ghost houses.

Why do ghosts always hang around in threes?
Because two's company, three's a shroud.

What do you call a maggoty corpse with nothing to do?
Bored stiff.

What do you get if you cross a witch's cat with a lemon?
Sour puss.

What do short-sighted ghosts wear?
Spooktacles or a moanocle.

What rides do ghosts like to go on at the fairground?
The scary-go-round and the roller-ghoster.

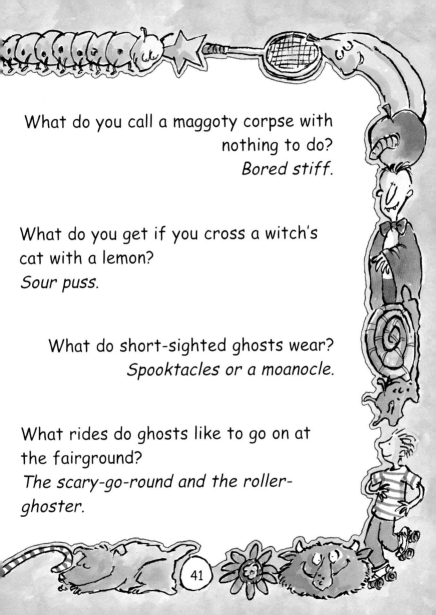

What do you get if you cross an ugly witch with a clown?
A frightful brew-ha-ha.

What does a ghost call his mum and dad?
Transparents.

Did you hear about the witch who invented a magic lift?
It's called a spell-e-vator.

What did the ghost say after he had been out haunting all night?
"I'm dead on my feet."

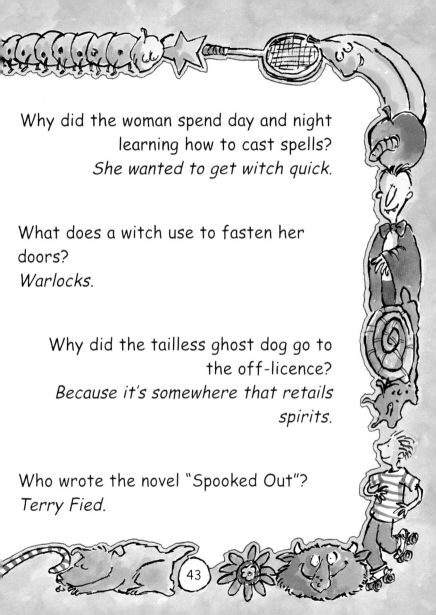

Why did the woman spend day and night learning how to cast spells?
She wanted to get witch quick.

What does a witch use to fasten her doors?
Warlocks.

Why did the tailless ghost dog go to the off-licence?
Because it's somewhere that retails spirits.

Who wrote the novel "Spooked Out"?
Terry Fied.

43

What did the bat say to the witch's hat?
"You go on ahead and I'll hang around."

What do you call a nervous witch?
A twitch.

Who do ghosts invite to their parties?
Polterguests.

How do ghosts like their eggs?
Terrifried.

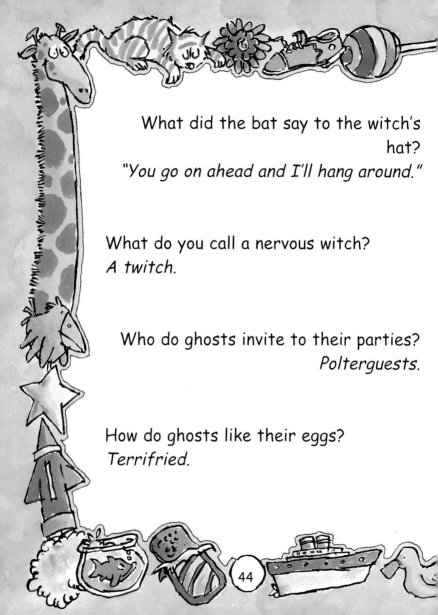

What do you say to stop a witch
laughing?
"Cut the cackle."

What do you call a sorceress waiting by the roadside with her thumb out?
A witchhiker.

What do you get if you cross a ghost with an owl?
Something that scares everyone but doesn't give a hoot.

What does a witch wear in the summer?
Open-toad sandals.

Why are ghosts no good at telling lies?
You can see right through them.

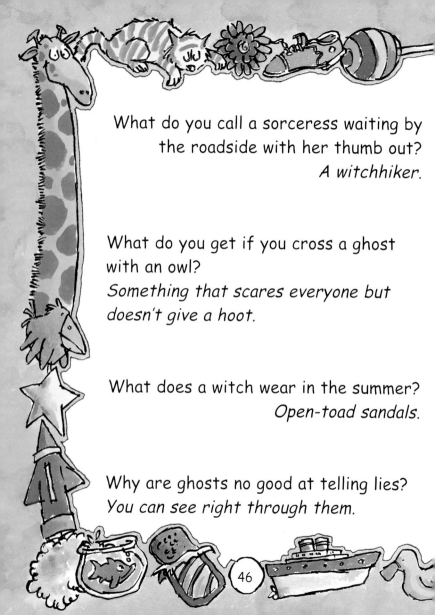

Why are ghosts such good teachers?
They go through things over and over again.

What does a sorceress wear to work?
A bewitching suit.

Why did the ghost's mail rattle?
It was a chain letter.

What did the ghost guard say?
"Who ghosts there?"

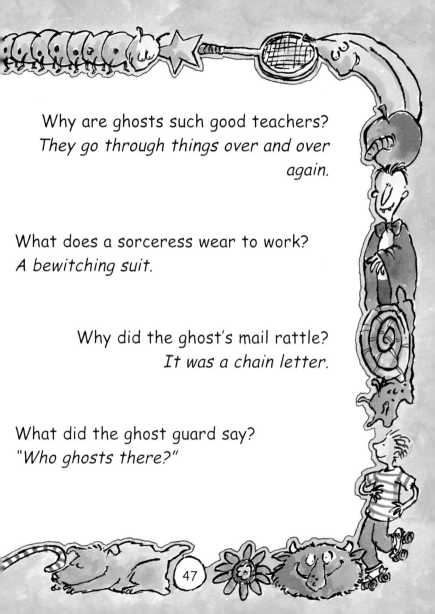

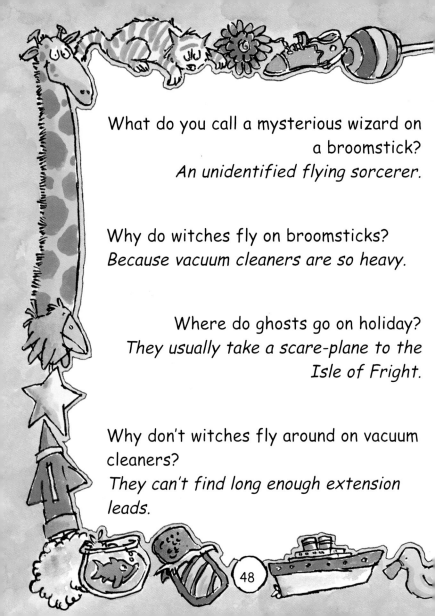

What do you call a mysterious wizard on a broomstick?
An unidentified flying sorcerer.

Why do witches fly on broomsticks?
Because vacuum cleaners are so heavy.

Where do ghosts go on holiday?
They usually take a scare-plane to the Isle of Fright.

Why don't witches fly around on vacuum cleaners?
They can't find long enough extension leads.

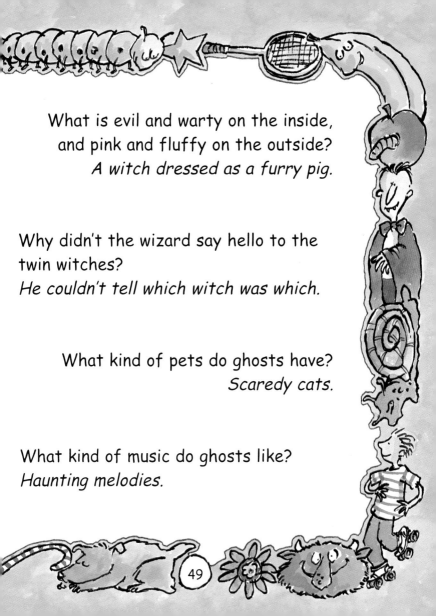

What is evil and warty on the inside,
and pink and fluffy on the outside?
A witch dressed as a furry pig.

Why didn't the wizard say hello to the
twin witches?
He couldn't tell which witch was which.

What kind of pets do ghosts have?
Scaredy cats.

What kind of music do ghosts like?
Haunting melodies.

Why did the witch wear a green, pointy hat?
So she could walk across snooker tables unnoticed.

What kind of ghosts haunt a hospital?
Surgical spirits.

What's evil and warty and bounces?
A witch on a spacehopper.

How can you tell if there's a ghost in
your bed?
There's a "G" on its pyjamas.

Where did the ghosts live in the Wild
West?
Tombstone.

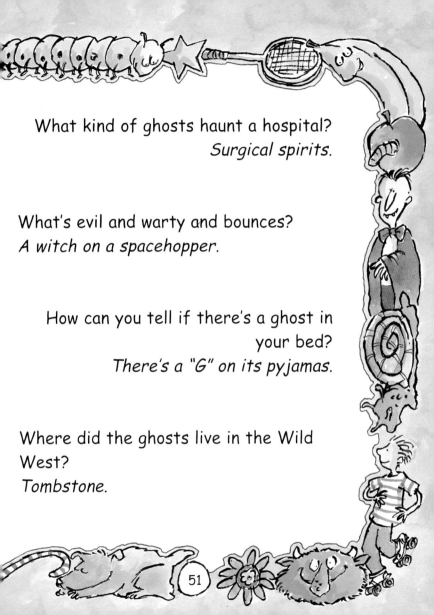

What has six legs and flies?
A witch and her cat on a broomstick.

What has two legs, a broom and flies?
A caretaker covered in jam.

Why did the witch wash her broomstick?
She wanted to make a clean sweep of it.

Where do foreign ghosts live?
In a distant terror-tory.

What kind of jewellery do witches wear?
Charm bracelets.

What do witches ring in a hotel?
B-room service.

Who turns the lights off at Halloween?
The light's witch.

Why did the ghost go to see an astrologer?
He wanted to see his horror-scope.

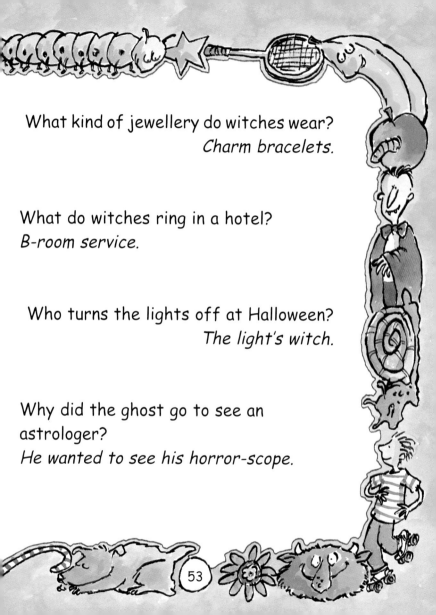

TROUBLESOME TIKES

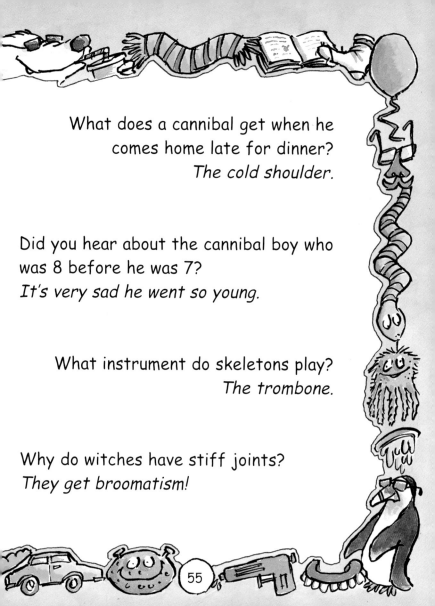

What does a cannibal get when he comes home late for dinner?
The cold shoulder.

Did you hear about the cannibal boy who was 8 before he was 7?
It's very sad he went so young.

What instrument do skeletons play?
The trombone.

Why do witches have stiff joints?
They get broomatism!

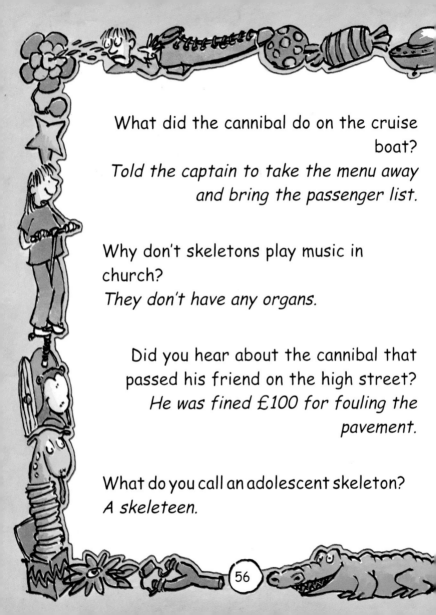

What did the cannibal do on the cruise boat?
Told the captain to take the menu away and bring the passenger list.

Why don't skeletons play music in church?
They don't have any organs.

Did you hear about the cannibal that passed his friend on the high street?
He was fined £100 for fouling the pavement.

What do you call an adolescent skeleton?
A skeleteen.

What did the skeleton say to the barman?
"A pint of beer and a mop, please."

Why shouldn't a cannibal eat eyeballs and brain on an empty stomach?
It's more polite to use a plate.

Why was the skeleton so thirsty?
He was bone dry.

Did you hear about the cannibal who loved Italian food?
He ordered a pizza with everybody on it.

Why did the sorceress buy a huge mansion?
Because she was so witch.

Why wouldn't the skeleton get a job?
He was bone idle.

What do cannibals eat for pudding?
Chocolate-covered aunts.

What kind of wine does a skeleton like?
One with plenty of body.

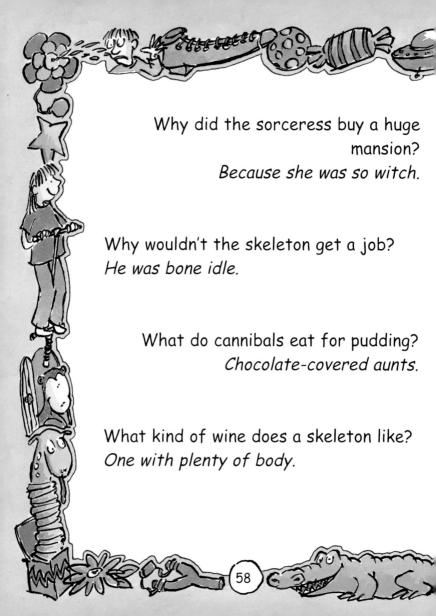

Why do skeletons wear thick coats?
If they don't, the wind goes straight through them.

What's a cannibal's favourite game?
Swallow the leader.

Why did the skeleton call off the wedding?
His heart wasn't in it.

What do you call a stupid skeleton?
Bonehead.

How did the sick witch get to hospital?
She flu.

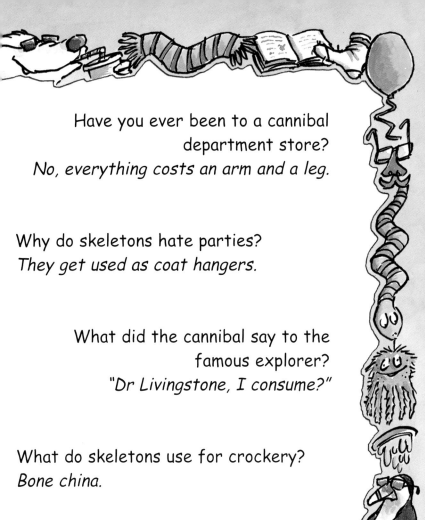

Have you ever been to a cannibal
department store?
No, everything costs an arm and a leg.

Why do skeletons hate parties?
They get used as coat hangers.

What did the cannibal say to the
famous explorer?
"Dr Livingstone, I consume?"

What do skeletons use for crockery?
Bone china.

Why did the skeleton go to jail?
He was bad to the bone.

Why didn't the cannibal like eating the clown?
He thought it tasted funny.

What do you say to terrify a skeleton?
"Here, Fido, din-dins!"

What does a cannibal eat with cheese?
Pickled organs.

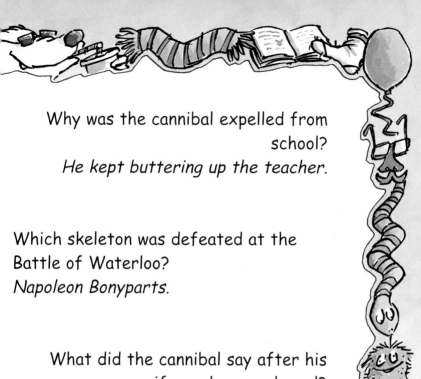

Why was the cannibal expelled from school?
He kept buttering up the teacher.

Which skeleton was defeated at the Battle of Waterloo?
Napoleon Bonyparts.

What did the cannibal say after his wife made a good meal?
"I'm really going to miss her."

Why are skeletons so calm?
Because nothing gets under their skin.

What do skeletons say before the start of a meal?

"Bone appétit."

What happened to the commander who was put in the chief cannibal's cooking pot?
He became commander-in-chief.

What kind of art do skeletons rave about?
Skullture.

What do cannibals do to their toughest foes?
Stick them in the microwave until they're tender.

How does a skeleton stop?
Vertebrakes.

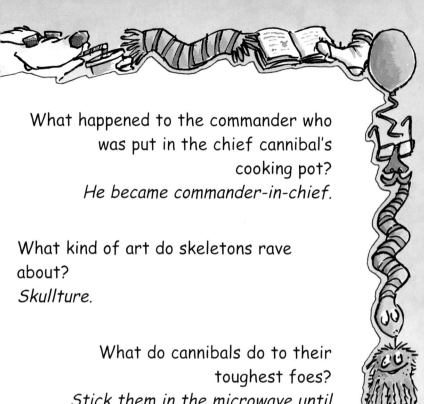

How did the skeleton know the cannibal was up to no good?
He could feel it in his bones.

What did the cannibal do in an "all you can eat" restaurant?
He ate two waiters and the chef.

What do you get if you cross a skeleton with a jar of peanut butter?
Extra-crunchy peanut butter.

What's the definition of a cannibal?
Someone who loves his fellow man — with gravy.

Why do you have to wait so long for a ghost train?
They only operate a skeleton service.

Why couldn't the cannibal boil the missionary in his pot?
Because he was a friar.

Why aren't there any famous skeletons?
Because they're such a bunch of nobodies.

How did skeletons in the Wild West get their mail?
The bony express.

How can you help a hungry cannibal?
Give him a hand.

How do you reach a skeleton when he's not at home?
Call his mobile bone.

What do cannibals call a line of people waiting at a bus stop?
A barbequeue.

Why are cemeteries always such noisy places?
All the coffin.

What's a skeleton's favourite kind of apple?
Coccyx.

What's a skeleton's favourite fruit?
Bone-anas.

What vegetable do skeletons like more than any other?
Marrow.

Why did the cannibal's daughter go to so many parties?
She was looking for an edible bachelor.

Why was the Scandinavian cannibal
a vegetarian?
He would only eat swedes.

How can you tell the difference
between a male and a female skeleton?
She's the one with the diamond ring.

Who is a skeleton's favourite pop star?
Bone-o.

What's the definition of a shocking noise?
A skeleton dancing on a tin roof.

What did the cannibal say when he was full?
"I couldn't eat another mortal!"

How do you spot a polite ghost?
It only spooks when spoken to.

Why didn't the scarecrow ever have any fun?
He was a stuffed shirt.

How do undertakers speak?
Gravely.

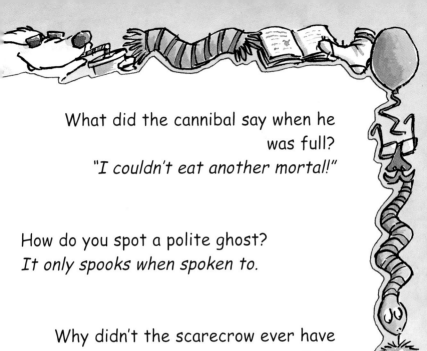

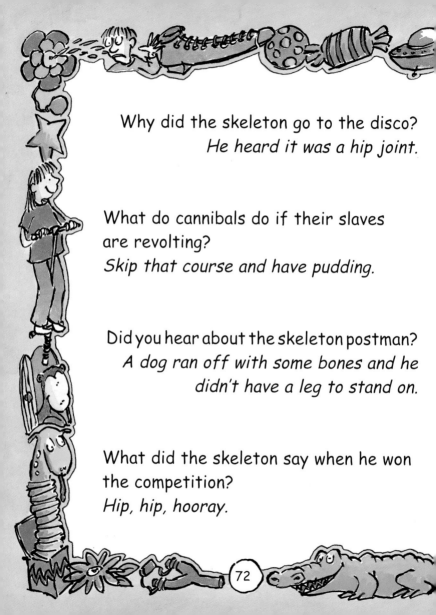

Why did the skeleton go to the disco?
He heard it was a hip joint.

What do cannibals do if their slaves
are revolting?
Skip that course and have pudding.

Did you hear about the skeleton postman?
*A dog ran off with some bones and he
didn't have a leg to stand on.*

What did the skeleton say when he won
the competition?
Hip, hip, hooray.

Why did the cannibal feel sick?
He ate someone who disagreed with him.

What sort of books do skeletons like?
Spine chillers.

Why did the cannibal come back from holiday with no arms or legs?
It was self-catering.

What made the moon pale?
The atmos-fear.

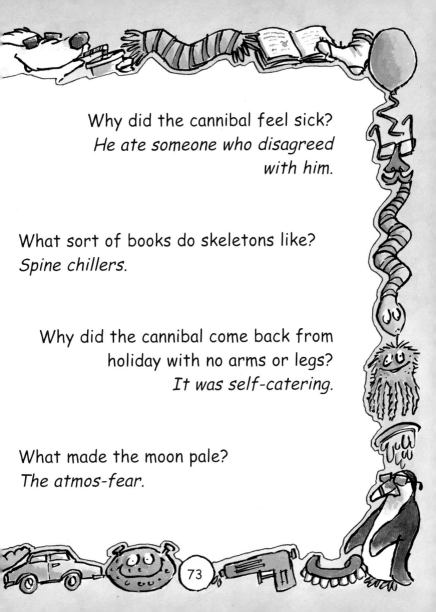

Why don't skeletons get along?
They've always got bones to pick with each other.

What happens if you upset a cannibal?
You get into hot water.

Who was the skeleton in the cupboard?
The winner of the great hide-and-seek competition of 1906.

What's huge, red and swims in the ocean?
Moby Bus.

Why did the cannibal get told off by his mother after he joked with a friend?
Because he was playing with his food.

What's a skeleton's favourite quotation?
"Tibia or not tibia, that is the question."

Who is the skeleton king of rock and roll?
Pelvis.

How do ghosts get out of the cemetery when it's locked?
They use a skeleton key.

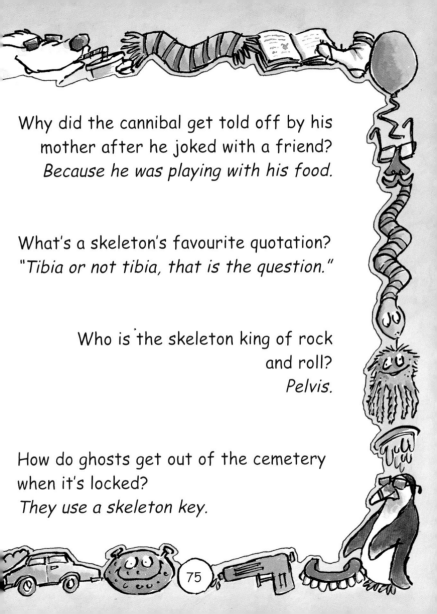

75

What did the cannibal make of his
new boss?
A casserole.

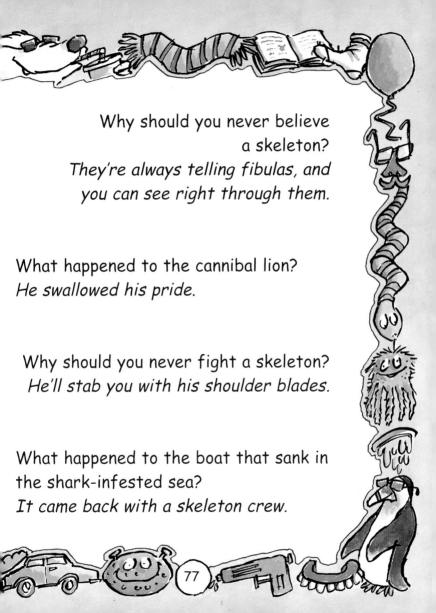

Why should you never believe
a skeleton?
*They're always telling fibulas, and
you can see right through them.*

What happened to the cannibal lion?
He swallowed his pride.

Why should you never fight a skeleton?
He'll stab you with his shoulder blades.

What happened to the boat that sank in
the shark-infested sea?
It came back with a skeleton crew.

What's a cannibal's favourite fast food snack?
A handburger.

Why do skeletons get away with murder?
The police can't pin anything on them.

Why did the cannibal catch a viper and dwarf?
He fancied a snake and pygmy pie.

What happened to the man who didn't pay the exorcist's bill?
He was repossessed.

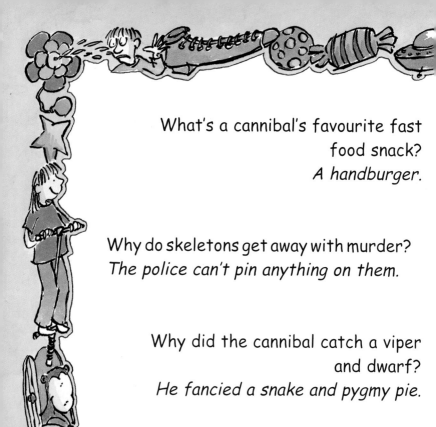

What sort of jokes do skeletons like?
Rib ticklers.

What did the cannibal say at his sugar plantation?
"I'll feed my lads with m'lasses!"

What do skeletons give their girlfriends on Valentine's Day?
Bone-bones in a heart-shaped box.

Why were the skeletons so happy after the party?
They had a rattling good time.

What do cannibals say to new acquaintances?
"Nice to eat you."

Why can't skeletons eat school dinners?
They don't have the stomach for it.

Why did the cannibal never go out?
He was fed up with other people.

Did you hear about the cannibal who didn't like his brother?
He just ate the chips.

What skeleton wears a kilt?
Boney Prince Charlie.

What happened at the cannibal wedding?
They toasted the bride and groom.

Why didn't the skeleton go to the party?
He had no body to go with.

What's very tall and says "Eef if of muf"?
A backwards giant.

Why couldn't the cannibal eat the batter?
He hadn't been bowled out yet.

What did the skeleton say to his girlfriend?
"I love every bone in your body."

Why do cannibals like clumsy people?
They just love butter fingers.

What's black, out of its mind and sits in trees?
A raven lunatic.

What do you call a skeleton who goes into the snow without a hat and scarf?
Numbskull.

What do health-conscious cannibals
eat?
Toe-fu.

What says, "Now you see me, now you
don't, now you see me, now you don't..."?
A skeleton on a zebra crossing.

Why do cannibals wash their hands
before dinner?
They won't eat dirty hands.

What's the definition of a coffin?
A snuff box.

Why is it no good trying to keep a
skeleton out of your house?
They have skeleton keys.

What do you call a skeleton snake?
A rattler.

How do you make a skeleton laugh?
Tickle its funny bone.

What do cannibals like on their toast?
Baked beings.

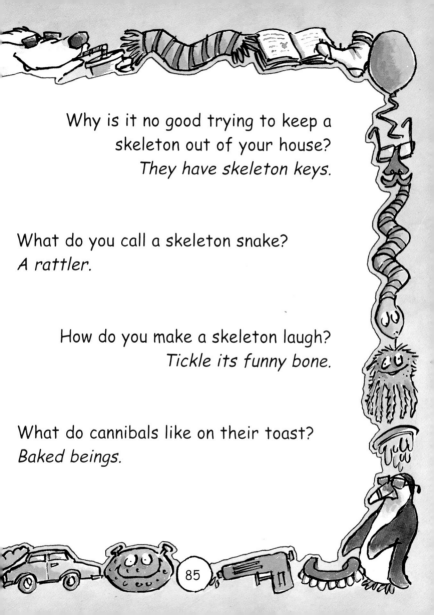

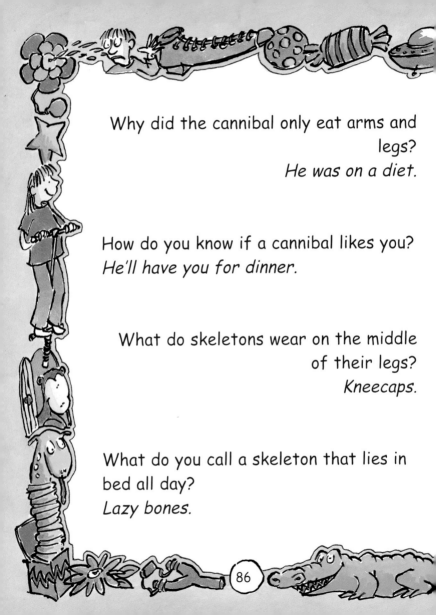

Why did the cannibal only eat arms and legs?
He was on a diet.

How do you know if a cannibal likes you?
He'll have you for dinner.

What do skeletons wear on the middle of their legs?
Kneecaps.

What do you call a skeleton that lies in bed all day?
Lazy bones.

What do you say to a cannibal family that has had burglars?
"Taste good?"

Why don't cannibals eat airmen?
Because they'll get wind.

Why don't cannibals eat sprinters?
Because they'll get the runs.

Where does it cost twenty pounds a head to eat?
At the Cannibal Café.

Where does a skeleton plug in its
electric toothbrush?
Its eye sockets.

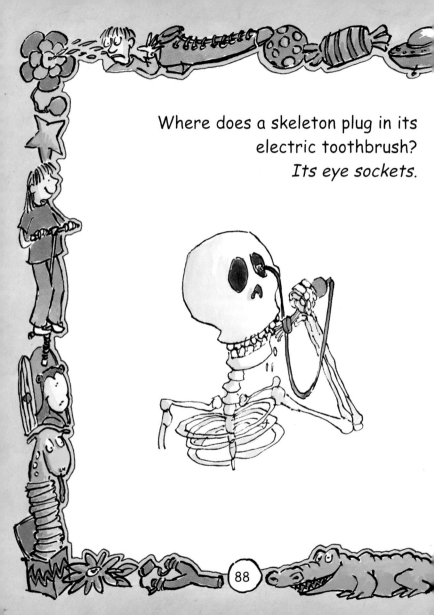

What does a cannibal have for breakfast?
Hard-boiled legs and soldiers.

What pop groups do skeletons most enjoy?
The Rolling Bones and Boney M.

Why was the cannibal sick after he ate the vicar?
You can't keep a good man down.

What space movie stars Count Dracula?
The Vampire Strikes Back.

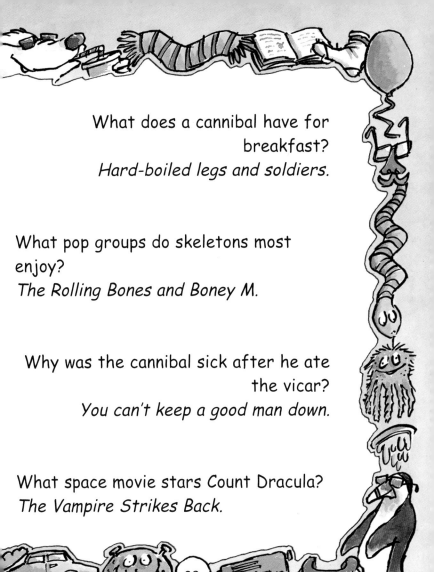

Why do skeletons seem so frightened?
It's as if they've just jumped out of their skins.

Why did the cannibal join the police force?
He wanted to grill the suspects.

Why wouldn't the skeleton do a bungee jump?
He had no guts.

What did the headless horseman ride?
A nightmare.

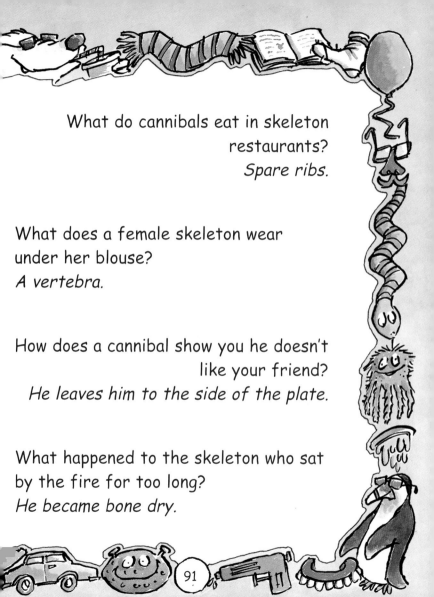

What do cannibals eat in skeleton restaurants?
Spare ribs.

What does a female skeleton wear under her blouse?
A vertebra.

How does a cannibal show you he doesn't like your friend?
He leaves him to the side of the plate.

What happened to the skeleton who sat by the fire for too long?
He became bone dry.

When do cannibals cook you?
On Fried-days.

Why did the skeleton go to hospital?
To have his ghoul stones removed.

What happened when the cannibal ate identical triplets, one after the other?
His meal repeated on him.

Why did the car stop when it saw a ghost?
It had a nervous breakdown.

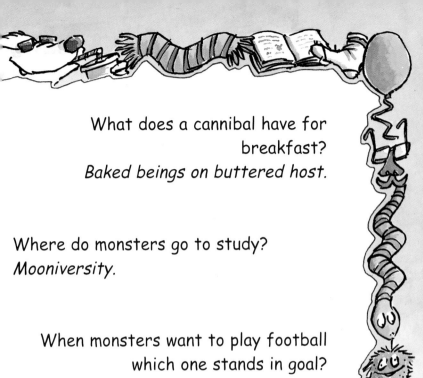

What does a cannibal have for breakfast?
Baked beings on buttered host.

Where do monsters go to study?
Mooniversity.

When monsters want to play football which one stands in goal?
The ghoulie.

What do you get when King Kong sneezes in your direction?
Out of the way.

What's a skeleton?
About 2000 skelepounds.

Why do cannibals ask for comedians
when they want a treat?
Because they go down really well.

Where do skeletons keep budgerigars?
Ribcages.

What happened when Godzilla took the
motorway into London?
His mum made him put it back.

When do cannibals leave the table?
When everyone's eaten.

What do cannibal secretaries do with leftover fingernails?
They file them.

What does a cannibal eat with curry?
Chut-knee.

Why did the two giant cyclopses get into a fight?
They couldn't see eye-to-eye.

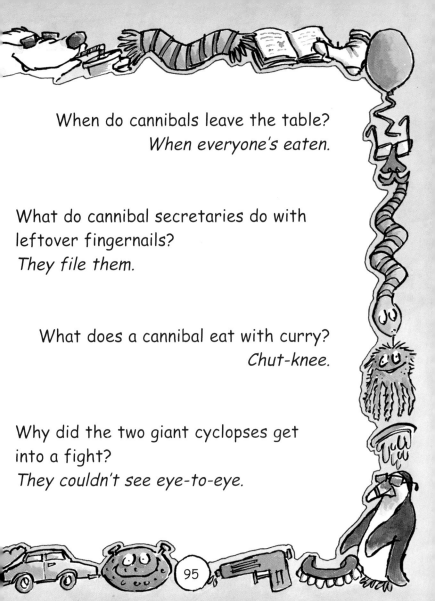

IMPISH
INCIDENTS

Do zombies eat popcorn with their fingers?
No, they eat the fingers separately.

What is a vampire's favourite sport?
Casketball.

Why does an imp get indigestion?
Goblin his food.

Why doesn't Dracula have any friends?
He's a pain in the neck.

What's a vampire's favourite fast food?
Someone with very high blood pressure.

Why did the witch feed her cat with pennies?
She wanted to put some money in the kitty.

What does a ghoul like most for breakfast?
Rice Creepies.

What do you get if you cross a vampire and a pygmy?
A pain in the knee.

What should you do if you like Dracula?
Join his fang club.

How do you join Dracula's fang club?
Send your name, address and blood group.

What did the vampire say to his victim?
"Your neck's on my list!"

Why was the vampire heartbroken?
His love was in vein.

What did the vampire say when he saw a victim sleeping peacefully?
"Ahh! Breakfast in bed!"

What do young zombies call their parents?
Mummy and Deady.

How did the vampire slayer make holy water?
She took some tap water and boiled the hell out of it.

What did Grandpa Ghoul say to his grandson when he hadn't seen him for ages?
"You gruesome!"

Why do vampires drink blood?
Fizzy drinks are bad for their fangs.

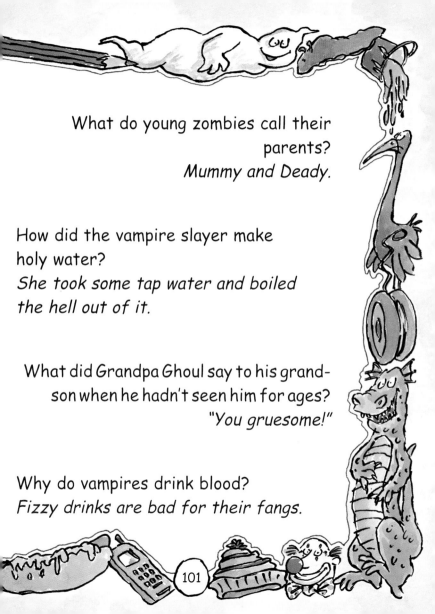

What on earth is as sharp as a
vampire's fang?
His other fang.

Why do vampires love school dinners?
They know they won't get steak.

What does a vampire fear most?
Tooth decay.

Why did Dracula take up acting?
It was in his blood.

Where did they put Dracula when he
was arrested?
In a blood cell.

What do you give a vampire with a sore
throat?
Coffin medicine.

What should you do if a zombie rolls his
eyes at you?
Pick them up and roll them back.

What groups do vampires join?
Blood groups.

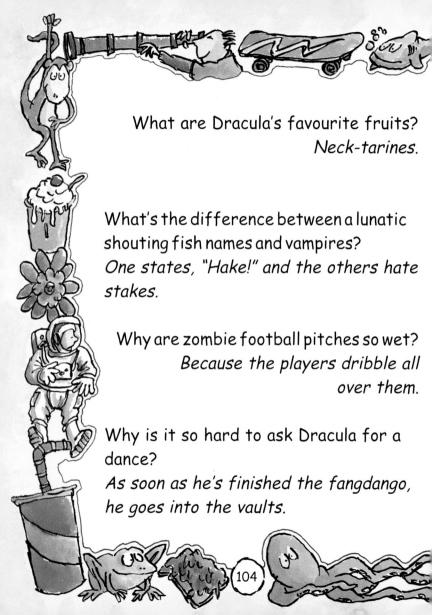

What are Dracula's favourite fruits?
Neck-tarines.

What's the difference between a lunatic shouting fish names and vampires?
One states, "Hake!" and the others hate stakes.

Why are zombie football pitches so wet?
Because the players dribble all over them.

Why is it so hard to ask Dracula for a dance?
As soon as he's finished the fangdango, he goes into the vaults.

How do devils protest?
In demon-strations.

What did the mummy vampire say to her screaming baby?
"Stop crying, you're driving me batty."

What happened when two rival vampire sects started fighting?
Fang warfare.

What is Dracula's favourite cocktail?
A Bloody Mary.

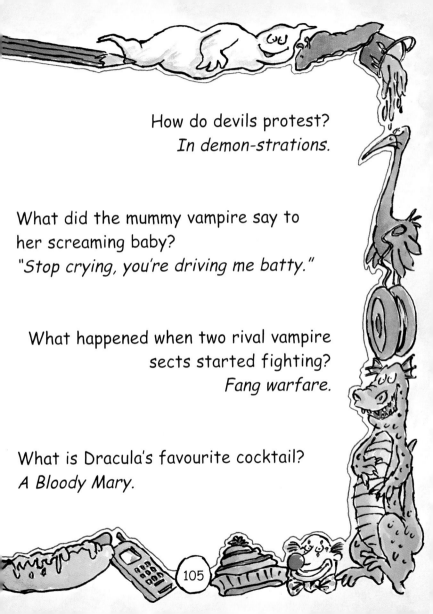

What do elves learn at school?
The elfabet.

When do vampires bite you?
On wincedays.

What's the best way to get rid of demons?
Plenty of exorcise.

What do vampires love to have for pudding?
Knickerbocker ghouly.

What's Dracula's favourite soup?
Scream of tomato.

What do you get if you cross a vampire
and a mummy?
A gift-wrapped bat.

What do you get if you cross a
werewolf and a vampire?
A fur coat that fangs around your neck.

Where do zombies stay on holiday?
*Anywhere that there's running rot and
mould in every room.*

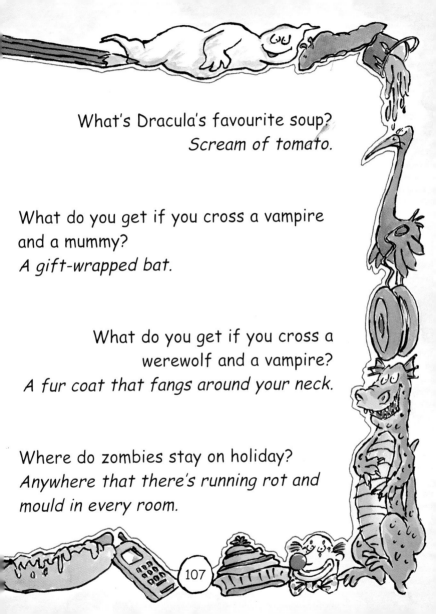

What does the baby vampire say before going to bed?
"*Turn on the dark. I'm afraid of the light.*"

What TV sitcom do demons never miss?
Fiends.

What does Dracula sing in the shower?
Fang you for the music.

Why do vampires take up skateboarding?
They think it's really ghoul, man.

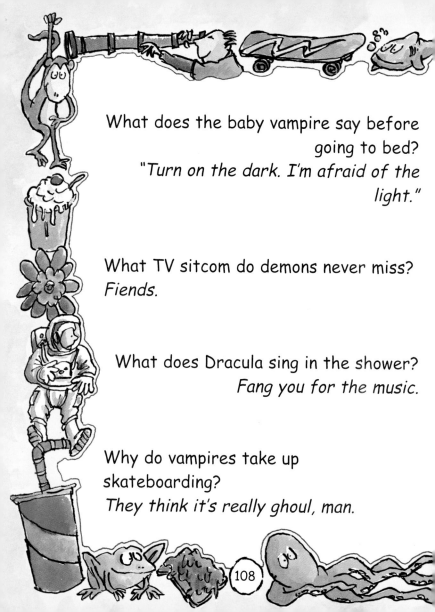

What do you call a bloodsucker who enjoys sleeping in the great outdoors? *A campfire vampire.*

Why do vampires have such good marriages?
They're batty about each other.

What do demons say when they meet in the morning?
"How the devil are you?"

Did you hear about the boxer who went looking for Dracula?
He was out for the count.

What do zombies wear in the rain?
Ca-ghouls.

Why is everybody bored of Dracula's artwork?
Because he always draws blood.

How do you know if a vampiress likes you?
She bats her eyes.

Where do vampires keep their savings?
In blood banks.

How do vampires cross the English Channel?
Blood vessels.

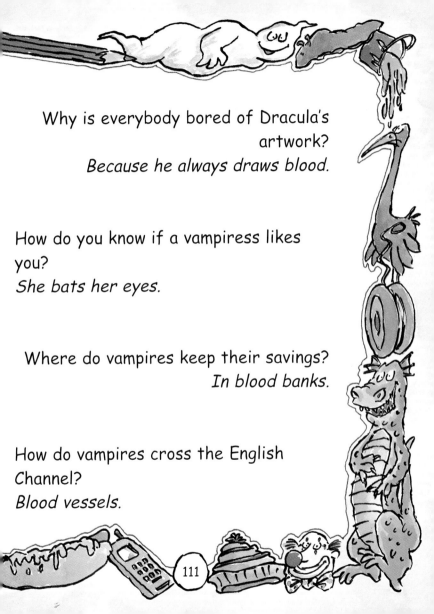

Why do demons and ghouls get on so well?
Because demons are a ghoul's best friend.

What kind of coffee do vampires order?
Decoffinated.

Who's the captain of the graveyard football team?
The ghoulie.

What position did the zombie play at netball?
Ghoul shooter.

What do vampire footballers have
at half-time?
Blood oranges.

Why can't vampires gamble?
*They run away when anyone puts
forward a stake.*

What happened when the vampire
bit a goose?
He felt down in the mouth.

What do vampires say when they kiss
each other?
"Ouch!"

113

Why did the football manager sign a horrible, blood-sucking beast?
Because his team needed a ghoul to win.

What's worse than bumping into a vampire?
Bumping into a thirsty vampire.

Why did the vampire come top of the class?
Because he passed his blood test.

Who has the most dangerous job in Transylvania?
Dracula's dentist.

What did the goblin say when he came home after a year abroad?
"Gnome sweet gnome."

What's the first thing a vampire bites after he gets his teeth checked?
The dentist.

What did the teacher say to Dracula after he failed his maths exam?
"Can't you Count Dracula?"

Why are monsters covered in wrinkles?
Have you ever tried to iron a monster?

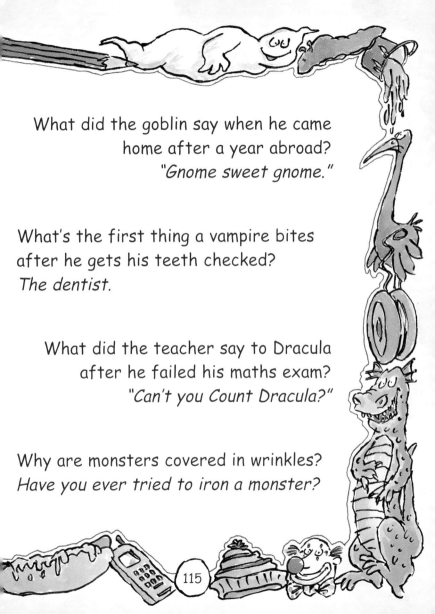

What do ghouls play during break time?
Corpse and robbers.

Why don't vampires argue?
Because they'd make themselves cross.

What type of imp is an excellent cook?
A hobgoblin.

What kind of vampire only bites people when they aren't looking.
A shy one.

Why do vampires have lentils, chickpeas
and beans with their meals?
Because they'll eat anything with pulses.

Why do zombies love mazes?
All the dead ends.

What comes out after dark and goes,
"Chomp, suck, ouch!"?
A vampire with a rotten tooth.

What do you get if you cross a vampire
with a 24-hour clock?
An all-day sucker.

Why is Dracula such a successful gymnast?
He loves the vault.

How did the vampire cure his sore throat?
By gargoyling.

Why are zombies so tired all the time?
They're dead on their feet.

What did Godzilla say after he had eaten London?
"What's for dinner?"

How can you tell if you've been bitten by a vampire?
Every time you have a drink, your neck leaks.

What do ghouls like to drink?
Demonade.

Why did Dracula recruit an apprentice?
*He thought he could do with some
new blood.*

Why do vampires make blood-curdling
screams?
*They're too runny to spread on their
toast otherwise.*

What would happen to a mummy if it
fell in the River Nile?
It would get wet.

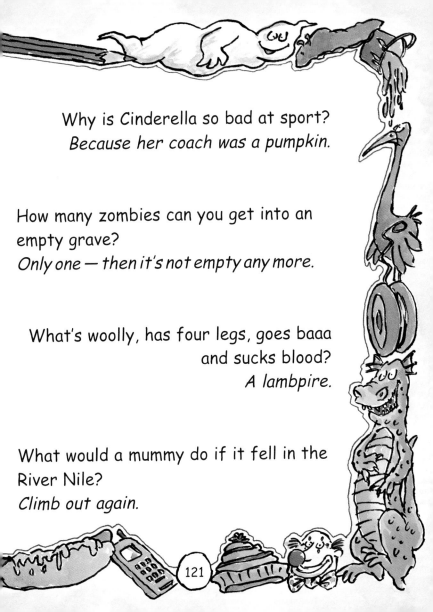

Why is Cinderella so bad at sport?
Because her coach was a pumpkin.

How many zombies can you get into an empty grave?
Only one — then it's not empty any more.

What's woolly, has four legs, goes baaa and sucks blood?
A lambpire.

What would a mummy do if it fell in the River Nile?
Climb out again.

What's sweet, red and doesn't like garlic?
A jampire.

What turns into a bat at midnight and goes oink?
A hampire.

What do you get if you cross a vampire with a songbird?
Draculark.

Where was Dracula when the lights suddenly went out?
In the dark.

How does a vampire clean his house?
With a victim cleaner.

What do you call zombie telephones?
Dead ringers.

What does Dracula do when he gets locked out of his castle?
He goes in through the bat flap.

What are the two things that a vampire can never have for breakfast?
Lunch and dinner.

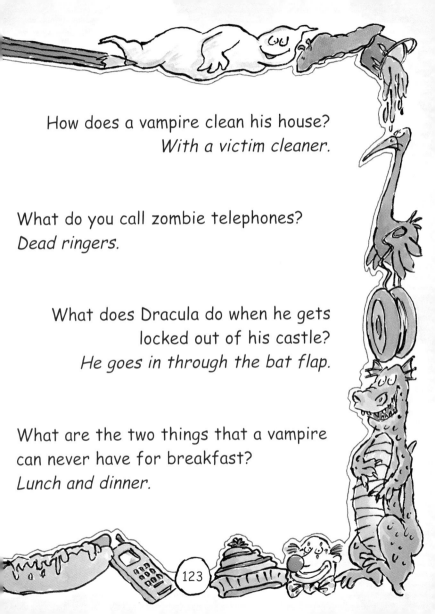

What do mad axe-men do at weekends?
Go chopping.

What does Dracula do when he's angry?
He flips his lid.

What's the difference between a computer and a vampire?
One has a byte of memory and the other has a memory of bites.

How do zombies smell?
Awful.

Who did the vampire want to marry?
The girl necks door.

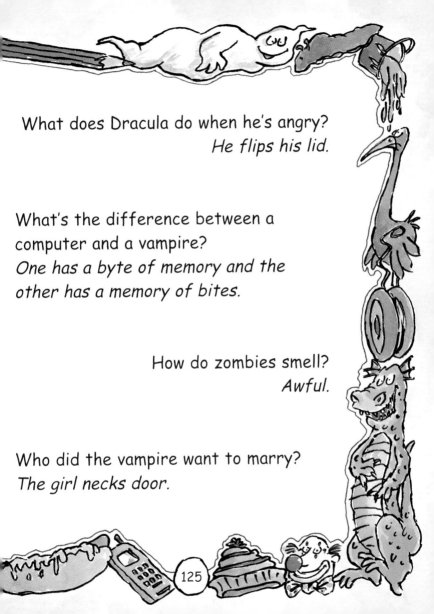

What beer do vampires drink?
Bloodweiser.

What did the zombie say to his girlfriend?
"What's up, gore-juice?"

What's a vampire's favourite animal?
A giraffe.

Why didn't the vampire need to spend much money on food?
He eats necks to nothing.

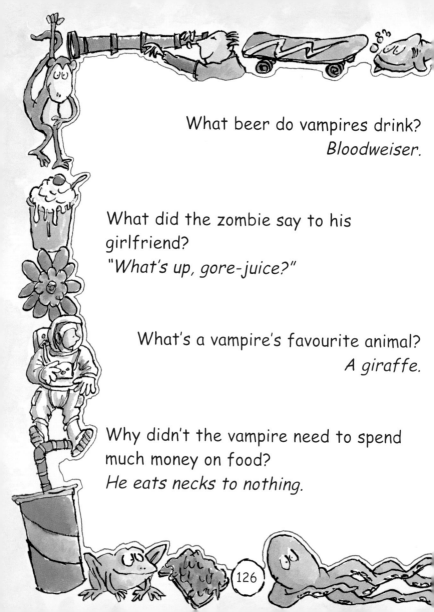

What is a vampire's favourite pudding?
Adam's apple pie.

Why was the damsel so tired after she went out with Dracula?
It was such a draining experience.

Why are vampire families so close?
Because blood is thicker than water.

What did the vampire conductor use?
A bat-on.

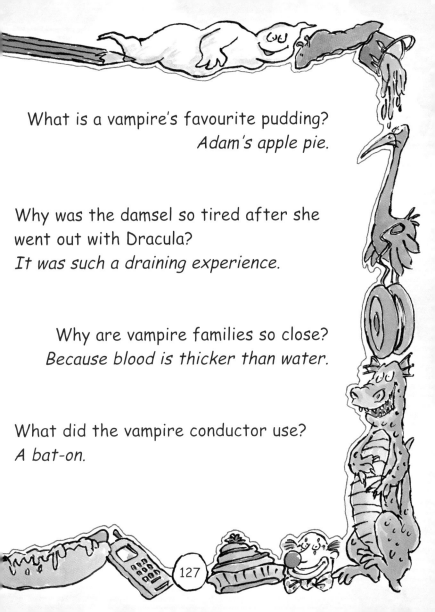

What's the difference between a
zombie and a doughnut?
Have you ever tried eating a zombie?

Why did the vampire go to
the audition?
*He wanted a part he could
get his teeth into.*

Why should you avoid a ghoul's garden
party?
It's a fête worse than death.

Why do vampires brush their teeth?
To prevent bat breath.

What happened at the vampire race?
It finished neck and neck.

What does a zombie have on his roast beef?
Gravey.

What did the vampire call his new false teeth?
A new-fangled device.

What is Dracula's favourite kind of sausage?
Fangfurters.

How do you know if a zombie has a glass eye?
It comes out in conversation.

What do you call a fat vampire?
Draculard.

What do zombies say as a magic word?
"Abracadaver!"

What kind of dinner would a vampire never order?
A stake dinner.

Why do ghouls use vampires to do the vacuum-cleaning?
Because they're great suckers.

Why did the vampire explode?
He hit an artery.

How many people go to a zombie's party?
Depends how many he can dig up.

Why are vampires like false teeth?
They come out at night.

What kind of pet does Dracula have?
A bloodhound.

What do you call an undead cow?
Zombeef.

Why does Dracula wear patent leather shoes?
Flip-flops don't look good with a cape and tuxedo.

How can you tell a vampire is such a fan of cricket?
He turns into a bat every night.

Where do Chinese vampires come from?
Fanghai.

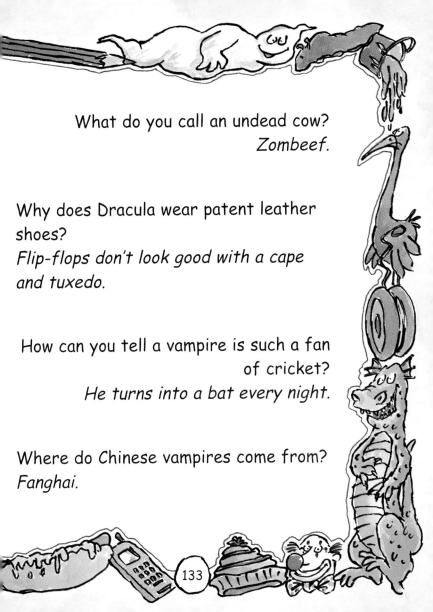

Where do zombies eat lunch?
At the cadaver-teria.

What screams till it gets what it wants
and flies away?
A spoiled bat.

What do you call an imp with a broken
leg?
Hoblin goblin.

What do you get if you cross a vampire
with a computer?
Love at first byte.

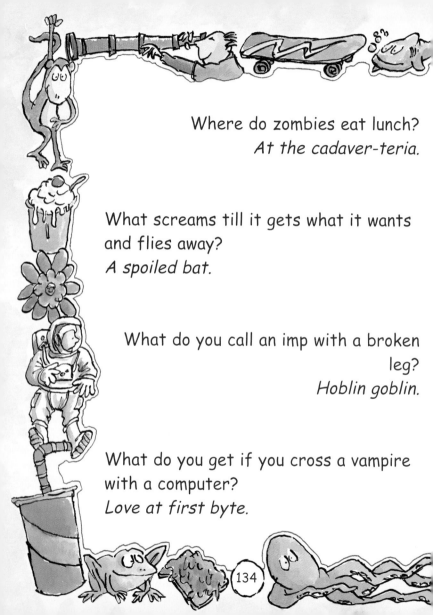

134

What happened at the vampire reunion?
All the blood relatives went.

What does Dracula say when he meets someone?
"I'd like to get to gnaw you."

Why are ghouls so hard to upset?
They know that every shroud has a silver lining.

What do goal keepers and vampires have in common?
They both have to look out for crosses.

What room does a zombie avoid?
The living room.

What happens when a vampire drinks too much?
He gets a fangover.

Why do bats fly at night?
Because they are afraid to drive.

Why did the festering zombie decide to stay in bed?
He felt rotten.

What is Dracula's favourite sport?
Bat-minton.

What do vampires have at 11 am?
A coffin break.

Which vampire almost bit James Bond?
Ghoulfinger.

What act do vampires most enjoy at the circus?
The jugulars.

Why did Dracula never get married?
He was a confirmed bat-chelor.

Where do vampires do their A levels?
High sghoul.

Why does Dracula always travel with his coffin?
Because his life is at stake.

What's the difference between a zombie and a butcher?
One stays awake and the other weighs a steak.

What did Dracula say after he saw a vampire film?
"That was fangtastic."

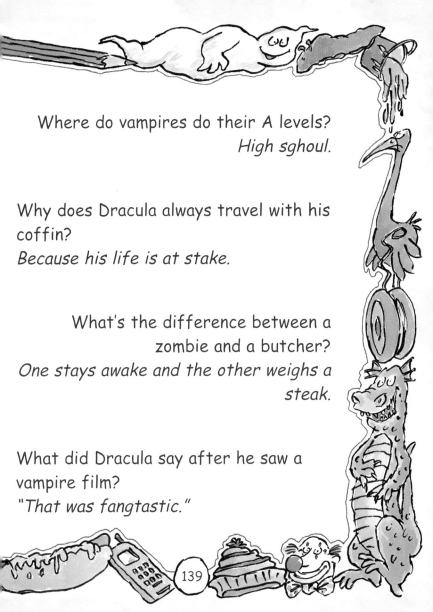

Why does nobody like Dracula?
He sucks.

What happened when Casanova turned into a vampire?
He became a neck-romancer.

Why was Dracula stopped from playing the piano?
His Bach was worse than his bite.

What is Dracula's favourite building?
The Vampire State Building.

140

Where do vampires wash?
In a bloodbath.

What do ghouls eat for breakfast?
Terrifried bread.

When the Devil's camera flash broke,
what sort of photos did he get back?
Prints of darkness.

What kind of monster can you put in
your washing machine?
A wash and werewolf.

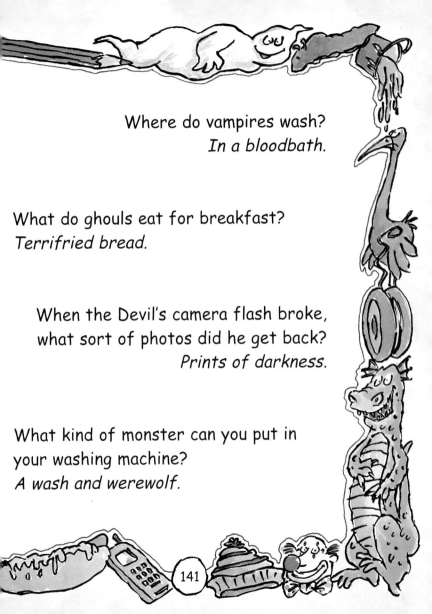

Why is Hollywood full of vampires?
They need someone to play the bit parts.

What trees do you find zombies sitting in?
Cemetrees.

Why did the vampire give his girlfriend
a blood test?
To see if she was his type.

What did the werewolf eat after he
had a tooth taken out?
The dentist.

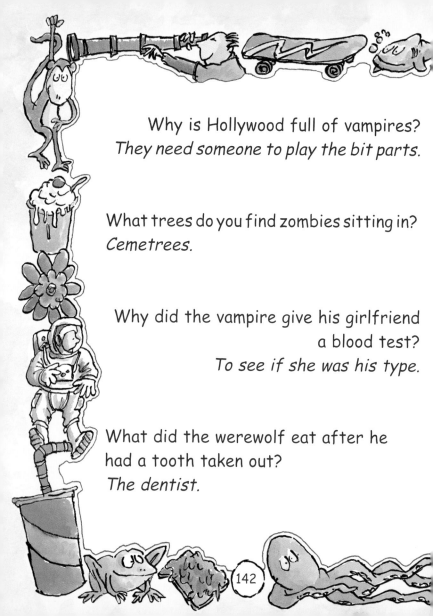

Did you hear about the hopeless vampire slayer?
He used pork chops because steaks were too expensive.

What do vampires eat with their apple pie?
Veinilla I-scream.

How do ghouls start their letters?
Tomb it may concern.

Where do vampires go fishing?
In a bloodstream.

What did the werewolf say when he saw Father Christmas?
"Yum yum."

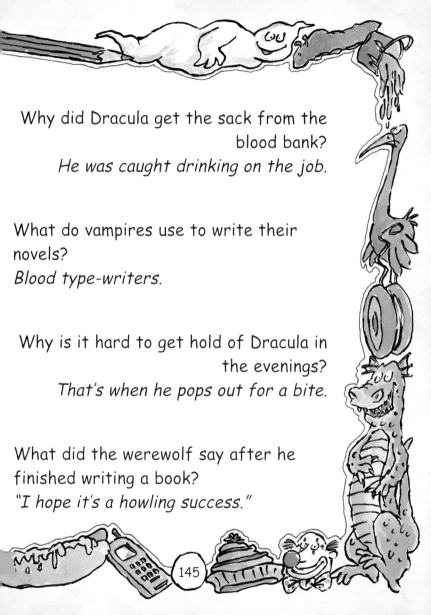

Why did Dracula get the sack from the blood bank?
He was caught drinking on the job.

What do vampires use to write their novels?
Blood type-writers.

Why is it hard to get hold of Dracula in the evenings?
That's when he pops out for a bite.

What did the werewolf say after he finished writing a book?
"I hope it's a howling success."

MONSTER MUNCH

Why did the monster eat a light bulb?
He fancied a light snack.

Why do dragons sleep during the day?
So they can fight knights.

How do you stop a monster biting his
nails?
Give him a bag of screws to chew on.

Why was the monster with sixteen
hands but no feet so clumsy?
He was all fingers and thumbs.

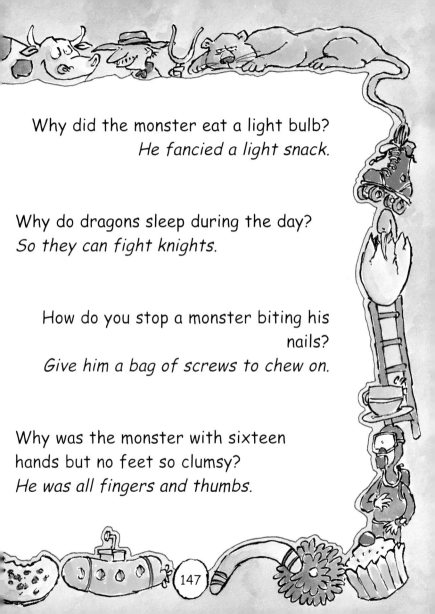

What's a monster's favourite play?
Romeo and Ghouliet.

What does Quasimodo use to iron his clothes?
A wok.

What does a slavering twenty-storey monster eat?
Anything it likes.

How can you tell that a monster's been in your bathroom?
The top's been left off the toothpaste.

Did you hear about the werewolf that
went bald in the war?
It happened in a hair raid.

Why was the little Egyptian boy so upset?
His daddy was a mummy.

What's the difference between a foul-
smelling, evil-breathed, slimy monster
and strawberries?
Everyone likes strawberries.

What time is it if a monster steps on
your car?
Time to buy a new one.

Why did the Cyclops have to close his school?
He only had one pupil.

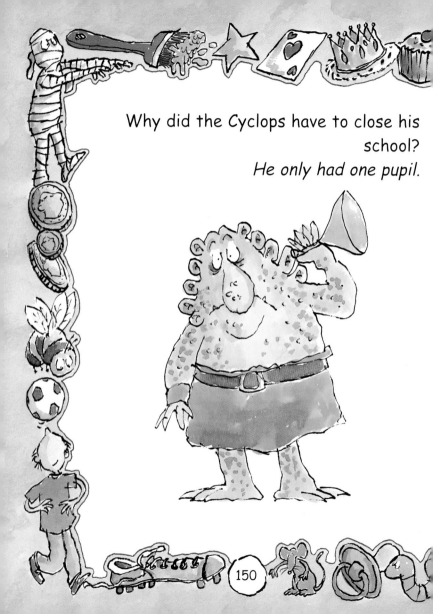

What kind of monster has the most ears?
The eeriest.

What do you call a monster with no neck?
The Lost Neck Monster.

What monster has never won the lottery?
The Luck Less Monster.

How do you get a dozen monsters in a chocolate box?
Take the chocolates out first.

What monster goes around ruffling people's hair?
The Locks Mess Monster.

Where do mummies go swimming?
The Dead Sea.

Why did the headless horseman go into business?
He wanted to get ahead in life.

What did Quasimodo shout to the kids chasing him down the road?
"I tell you, I don't have your football!"

Did you hear about the man who used to
be a werewolf?
He's much better noooooooow!

How do we know that Dr Frankenstein
was a very funny man?
He had his monster in stitches.

What do monsters call busy swimming
pools?
Soup.

Where do you find monster snails?
On the end of monsters' fingers.

Why was Dr Frankenstein so popular?
He was an expert at making new friends.

What kind of monster has one eye and rides a bike?
Cycle-ops.

What's the best way to raise a baby monster that's been abandoned by its parents?
With a crane.

What did the monster say to his family when he came home with a sack full of gnus?
"Have I got gnus for you!"

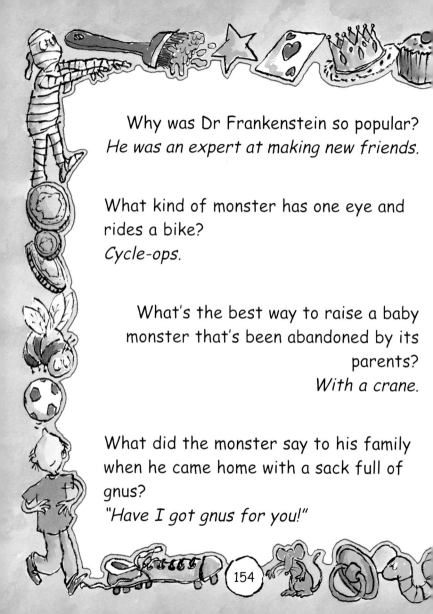

Why is Frankenstein's monster so easily agitated?
Because he has amps in his pants.

Why couldn't Swamp Thing go to the party?
Because he was bogged down at work.

What do you call a yeti that does a hundred sit-ups a day?
The abdominal snowman.

What do you call a yeti that's always late?
The abominable slowman.

What's hairy and hangs off the Empire State Building stinking of rotten eggs?
King Pong.

What do sea monsters eat?
Fish and ships.

Why did the vicar call the werewolf "Fixit"?
He kept doing little jobs around the churchyard.

Where does King Kong sit in the cinema?
Anywhere he likes.

What do mummies use for make up?
Nile varnish.

What's the best way to get in touch with a sea monster?
Drop it a line.

Why did the monster ask to leave the table?
He'd already eaten the fridge, the cooker and the kitchen cabinets.

How do you make a werewolf stew?
Keep it waiting for a few hours.

Did you hear about the monster with five legs?
His trousers fit him like a glove.

Why does Frankenstein's monster get indigestion?
He bolts down his food.

Why was the sea monster so upset?
The sea weed.

What sort of music do mummies like best?
Wrap.

What invention enabled Dr Frankenstein to walk through walls?
The door.

What do monsters call children on roller blades?
Meals on wheels.

What should you do if a werewolf bites your foot off?
Keep out of the kitchen — you'll make a terrible mess on that clean floor.

What is terrifying, hairy and drinks from the wrong side of the glass?
A werewolf with hiccups.

Where do werewolves live?
Werehouses.

How does a werewolf sign off his letters?
Best vicious.

What's wrapped in cling film and terrorizes Paris?
The lunch-pack of Notre Dame.

What giant monster goose terrorizes China?
Honk Kong.

What's green, very tall and mopes in the corner?
The Incredible Sulk.

What happened when the werewolf swallowed a clock?
He got ticks.

How do you stop a monster digging up your garden?
Take his spade away.

How do you know if the bogeyman is in your house?
All the tissues are missing.

How did the hideous mutant monster count to 112?
On his fingers.

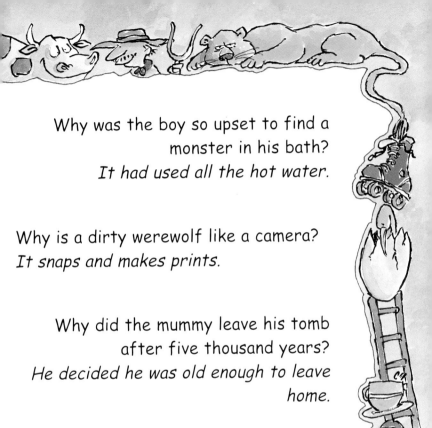

Why was the boy so upset to find a
monster in his bath?
It had used all the hot water.

Why is a dirty werewolf like a camera?
It snaps and makes prints.

Why did the mummy leave his tomb
after five thousand years?
*He decided he was old enough to leave
home.*

Why did the hungry vampire cross the
road?
To bite someone on the other side.

What's the difference between a werewolf and a cucumber?
I won't be asking you to do my shopping, if you don't know.

Did you hear about the monster that had an eye for the ladies?
He kept it in his back pocket.

What happened to the monster that took the five o'clock train home?
He had to give it back.

Why do mummies have trouble making friends?
They're too wrapped up in themselves.

Why did the invisible man look in the mirror?
He wanted to make sure he wasn't there.

Why did the monster relish Chinese boats?
He loved eating junk food.

What should you do if a monster borrows your bicycle?
Let him take it for as long as he wants.

What do you get if King Kong steps on Batman and Robin?
Flatman and Ribbon.

Why shouldn't you let a werewolf into your house?
They leave hairs all over the sofa.

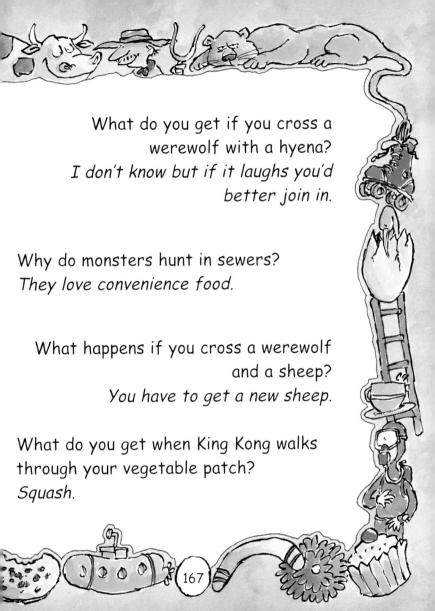

What do you get if you cross a
werewolf with a hyena?
*I don't know but if it laughs you'd
better join in.*

Why do monsters hunt in sewers?
They love convenience food.

What happens if you cross a werewolf
and a sheep?
You have to get a new sheep.

What do you get when King Kong walks
through your vegetable patch?
Squash.

What sort of fur do you get from a werewolf?
As fur away as possible.

What business is King Kong in?
Monkey business.

Why is it a bad idea to yank a werewolf's tail?
It might be a werewolf's tail, but it's surely the end of you.

What is even more invisible than the invisible man?
The invisible man's shadow.

What has two wheels, fourteen arms,
five heads and a bell?
A monster on a bicycle.

How scared was the little dog when it
saw a monster?
Terrierfied.

How does a werewolf move?
In vicious circles.

Why did Frankenstein stick his finger in
the plug socket?
He was interested in current events.

What do you get if King Kong falls down a mine shaft?
A flat miner.

What do you call a snarling ten-foot monster with tentacles and razor-sharp teeth?
"Your most wondrous majesty!"

What do monsters use when they shop?
Body bags.

What do monsters like to eat for breakfast?
Ham and legs.

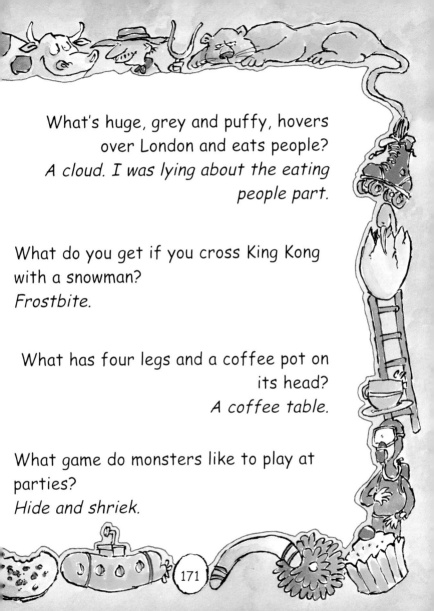

What's huge, grey and puffy, hovers over London and eats people?
A cloud. I was lying about the eating people part.

What do you get if you cross King Kong with a snowman?
Frostbite.

What has four legs and a coffee pot on its head?
A coffee table.

What game do monsters like to play at parties?
Hide and shriek.

What do monsters have if they catch someone breaking into their home?
Ham burglers.

How does a werewolf decorate a Christmas tree?
With furry lights.

Why are monsters so smelly?
Have you ever tried bathing a monster?

What did the monster say after he had been to the opticians?
"I have 20-20-20 vision."

Why did the monster feel like a million dollars?
It was green and wrinkly.

What fruit does Godzilla like to munch on?
The Big Apple.

What happened when the overweight monster raced the Incredible Hulk?
One ran in short bursts, the other ran in burst shorts.

How is a werewolf like a computer?
They both have kilobytes.

Why are mummies good spies?
They know how to keep things under wraps.

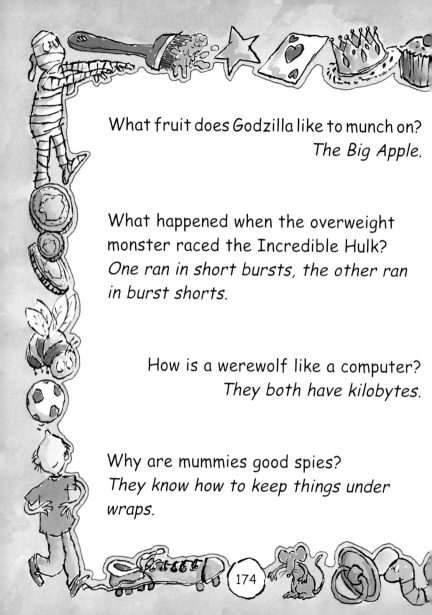

What should you give to a werewolf as a parting gift?
A comb.

What do you find between King Kong's toes?
Slow runners.

Why was the monster surprised to find turnips growing out of his ears?
He thought he'd planted parsnips.

How can carrying a torch stop a monster from attacking you?
If you carry it very, very fast.

What happened when Frankenstein's monster lost his girlfriend?

He went to pieces.

What do you get if you cross a cow with a werewolf?

A hamburger that bites back.

What did Frankenstein's monster say when he was struck by lightning?

"Ahhh! That felt great!"

What kind of raincoat does Frankenstein wear when he's out in the rain?

A wet one.

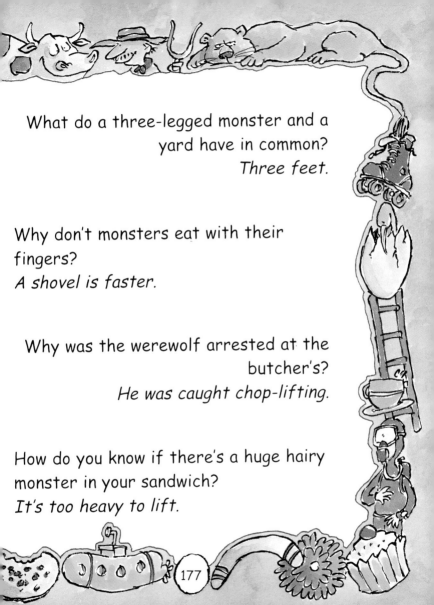

What do a three-legged monster and a yard have in common?
Three feet.

Why don't monsters eat with their fingers?
A shovel is faster.

Why was the werewolf arrested at the butcher's?
He was caught chop-lifting.

How do you know if there's a huge hairy monster in your sandwich?
It's too heavy to lift.

Why was Quasimodo such a good detective?
Because he had a hunch.

Why was the mummy so anxious?
He was wound up.

Why wouldn't the mummy go on holiday?
He didn't want to unwind.

Why did it take the monster all day to finish a book?
He wasn't very hungry.

What do you call a mummy that's falling
to bits?
Crummy.

What do monsters eat at rush hour?
Traffic jam.

What has fur and flies?
A dead werewolf.

What do you call a clean, tidy and well-
behaved monster?
A failure.

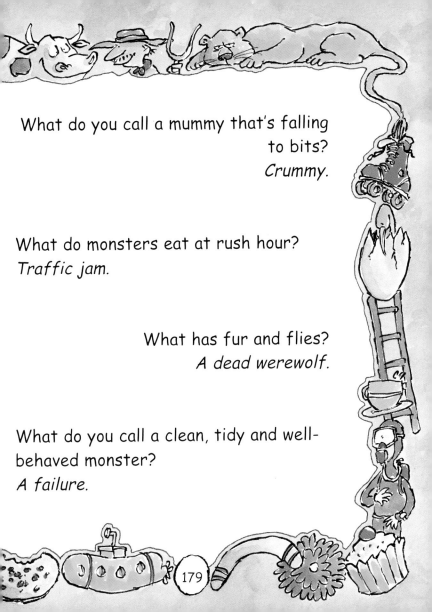

What do you call a friendly mummy?
Chummy.

What kind of monster makes sure you change your underwear and puts you to bed at night?
A mummy.

How do mummies hide?
They wear masking tape.

What do you get if you cross a monster with a supercomputer?
A huge, hairy genius.

What did the policeman say to the
three-headed monster?
"Hello, hello, hello!"

What happened to the monster that ate
plutonium?
It got atomic ache.

What do you call a drunken werewolf?
Whino.

Why did the monster have to scratch
itself?
Nobody else knew where it itched.

Why do werewolves have lots of matted fur?
They think they look daft in plastic macs.

Where did Dr Frankenstein find the
head for his monster?
Bolton.

What runs in monster families?
Noses.

Why did the ugly, slimy, stinky monster
go to bed early?
It wanted its beauty sleep.

How can you mend King Kong's arm if
he's twisted it?
With a monkey wrench.

Where are most werewolf films made?
Howlywood.

What time does a monster duck wake up?
The quack of doom.

Why do monsters lie down?
To trip up low-flying aircraft.

Why did the huge, hairy monster wear brown boots?
His black ones were being repaired.

How do you stop a foul, sweaty monster from smelling?
Cut off its nose.

Why do baby monsters travel by rail?
They love chew-chew trains.

What beasts are related to werewolves?
Whenwolves and whywolves.

How do you talk to a giant?
Use big words.

What goes "Ha, ha, ha, ha, bonk, bonk, bonk"?
A monster laughing its heads off.

What happened when the boy monster met the girl monster?
It was love at first fright.

What did the Loch Ness Monster say to his friend?
"Long time no sea."

What board game do monsters like to play?
Monstropoly.

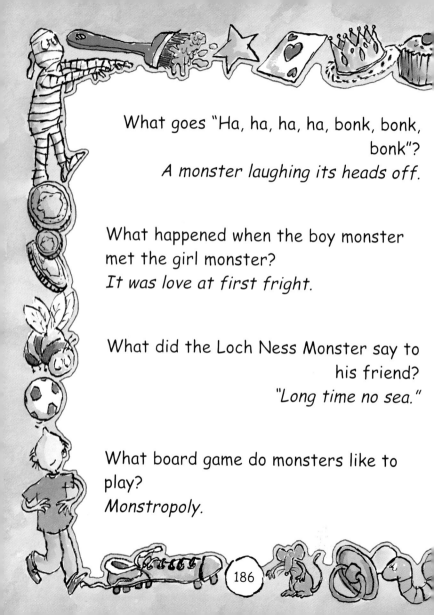

What can a monster do that you can't?
Rub his tummy, pat his head, and blow his noses at the same time.

What should you do with a blue monster?
Try to cheer it up.

What kind of monster stamps letters and polishes shoes?
Frank 'n' shine.

What did the monster do when he lost his head?
Called a head hunter.

What kind of monster is a leading
quantum physicist?
Frank Einstein.

What's the difference between a
werewolf and a flea?
*A werewolf can have fleas, but a flea
can't have a werewolf.*

If the cavemen lived in the Stone Age,
when did the mummies live?
The bandage.

What's the last thing a monster takes
off before it goes to bed?
Its feet off the floor.

What should you do with a green monster?
Put it in the sun until it ripens.

How do you teach a monster manners?
Tell it not to talk with someone in its mouth.

Why don't monsters eat penguins?
Because they can't get the wrappers off.

What happened when the canary flew into Godzilla's mouth?
Shredded tweet.

What's the difference between a monster and an elephant?
Monsters have terrible memories.

What do you call a witch in a horsehair shirt?
Itchy witchy.

What do ghosts eat for breakfast?
Dreaded wheat.

How do ghosts contact each other when they're out of the house?
Cellular moans.

When is a huge, hairy monster most likely to get into your house?
When the door is open.